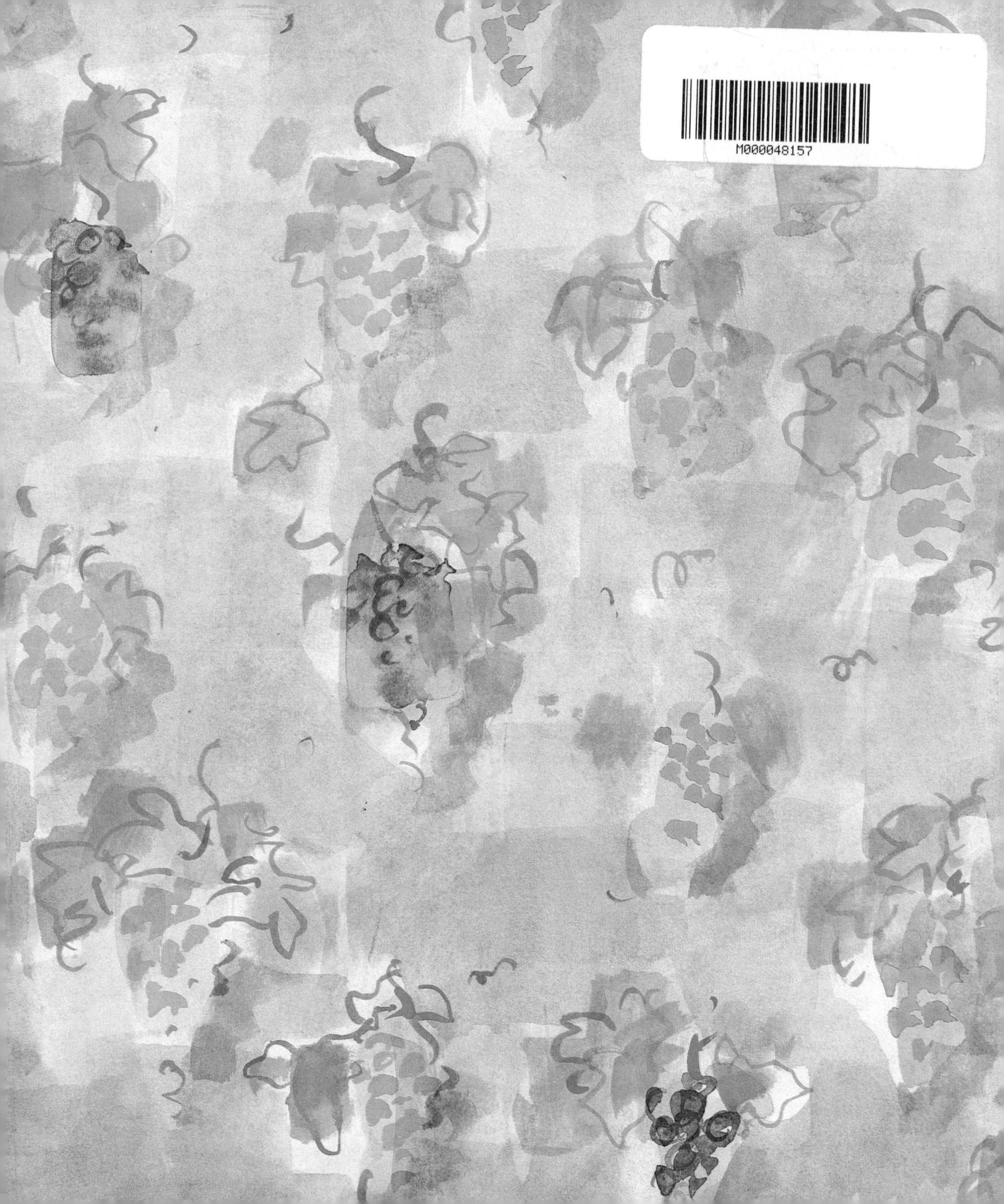

RECIPES
was produced and edited
by Imogen Bright and Vanessa
Whinney.

Designer: Sara Mathews
Artist: Binny Mathews
Author: Sara Mathews

First published in Great Britain by
Eyebright Publications, 21 Weedon Lane,
Amersham, Bucks HP6 5QT, 1988.

ISBN 0 948751 02 9

This book was set in Garamond by Kelmscott
Press Limited, London.
Reproduction by Fotographics.
Printed and bound in Portugal by Printer Portuguesa.

Recipes

A Notebook for Cooks

CONTENTS

INTRODUCTION

Have you ever wished you had somewhere to record all those recipes, hints and cookery tips that have so often gone astray just when you needed them? Here is the answer – your own book in which to note all these and much more, so that you have at your finger tips everything you require for quick meals and special occasions to delight both your family and guests. Then, after a happy and relaxed session in your kitchen, you can modestly acknowledge their compliments.

You will be creating your own very personal cookbook if you add notes of taste combinations, new methods, ideas for emergencies, and records of when you cooked a dish, with ideas for improvements. Used in this way, it could help you to develop a distinctive style with your own special tips.

This book is divided into five main sections: Soups and Starters, Light Dishes, Main Courses, Desserts and Other Dishes, in which to write down or paste in your own choice of recipes. Why not collect these from friends whose dinner parties have inspired you, from your travels, from magazines and newspapers, and from radio and television programmes? The book is also a convenient place to write down the page numbers in other cookbooks where more of your favourite recipes are to be found.

These pages contain helpful tips to whet your appetite, and to provide you with useful information. At the back of the book, there is a short section of basic recipes followed by a page for your wine notes, a herb chart and other useful

cookery information. The blank index on pages 136-140 can be filled in as you gather recipes, providing a quick reference to the sections, which are very versatile. They give plenty of scope for all cooks, including vegetarians.

Cooking is an art form. The Chinese have cultivated this art, which to them is more a way of life, by taking immense care and pleasure with texture, taste, colour combinations and the balance of moist or dry foods. They appreciate individual ingredients for their special properties and for what they can contribute to a meal. Many great chefs design their menus according to which fresh foods are in season at the market. With their intuitive sensitivity, they can conjure up the taste of a particular food and what will best complement it, thereby inventing an exciting new dish from the highest quality produce available at that time.

One of the reasons why cooking is so satisfying is because it gives an outlet for your creative gifts. Trying out different food combinations will give you an entirely new perspective. With just a limited selection of foods, for instance wild mushrooms, pork, spinach, carrots and oranges, you can work out several different menus. These examples show how versatile individual ingredients can be:

Spinach soup
Pork sauté with mushrooms
Carrot and orange cake

Carrot and orange salad
Pork and spinach casserole
Wild mushroom savoury

Spinach ravioli with mushroom sauce
Roast pork and glazed carrots
Chilled orange soufflé

Cooking should always be fun, and sharing a good meal with friends or family might be compared to listening to a superbly played piece of music or looking at a beautiful painting. We can easily get habit-bound in our style of cooking. Experimentation is the answer. Keep an open mind about different tastes and flavours, and when you are away from home, bring back recipes and ingredients. Unusual foods are not always outrageously expensive, and can make your cooking more exciting. In eating, as with other fashions, there is now much greater diversity. Even French chefs, who never used to deviate from their classical training, have introduced new concepts in cooking, taking their ideas from other cultures, for example China and Japan, the Middle East and South America.

The presentation of food, as well as the quality of taste, needs careful throught. Garnishes do not have to be very elaborate. A simple sprig of herbs on a savoury dish or a dusting of icing sugar on a dessert can be most attractive. Interesting china and dishes will complement and display your cooking to the best effect. It is fun to use a variety of decorative plates in different colours for each of your courses. Desserts or starters, served in something original such as pretty tea cups, or even on blocks of wood or stone *à la japonaise*, can look more appetizing and exciting, and provide a conversational stimulus as well.

When you are cooking, make sure you are relaxed and have time to really concentrate on the details. It will help if you check that there is nothing you have to do beforehand such as soaking beans. Think about the order in which you work so that you make the best use of available space, and get out all the ingredients before you start. Try to wash up as you go along so that you keep the working surfaces clear. Anticipate that new untried recipes may take longer than expected. Some dishes improve with keeping, and can be cooked several days in advance, while others need last minute preparation or finishing touches, so make sure that you do not have too many which need your immediate attention in one meal.

It is useful to collect some special recipes for dishes which are quick or expandable, in case you are showered with unexpected guests. It is also a good idea to enter tips for dishes that can be concocted in an emergency from your store cupboard.

In this book we have given imperial and metric as well as American measures, but if you need to make any conversions for your own recipes, you can refer to the charts at the back.

Happy Cooking!

SOUPS & STARTERS

Starters are important because they set the tone of the meal and whet the appetite. They should be light, and the helpings not too large. Balance the first course with the dishes which are to follow. You can serve anything as a starter, remembering that elaborate, rich recipes are not necessarily the best cooking. A simple salad can give as much pleasure as something which has taken hours to prepare. It is the quality of the ingredients that counts. The experience of tasting asparagus which has been picked at its peak, and then prepared, cooked and served simply, is hard to beat. Its elegance and beautiful colour are visually satisfying, and its aroma stimulates the senses in anticipation of delights to follow.

If you have some favourite party ideas, record them here as well as soups and starters. They are often interchangeable with appetizers, and simple ideas such as crudités – neatly cut sticks of raw vegetables dipped in a variety of mayonnaise or yoghurt based sauces – can also be served at parties or with pre-theatre drinks.

It makes all the difference to add simple but pretty garnishes to the first course. Serve elegantly cut lemon wedges with grilled sardines, add a poached egg to a warm salad, make croutons or toast for hot soups, and herb ice cubes for cold soups. For a warm summer evening, try something unusual and make a chilled fruit soup garnished with edible flowers, or a Bloody Mary sorbet decorated with frosted mint leaves.

Asparagus is such a perfect vegetable that it is usually served as a separate course, needing only butter and seasoning. Peel any tough stems with a potato peeler and tie in bundles with string. Do not immerse the tips in the boiling water. With a lid on the pan the steam will do the rest. If you want to serve it cold, cool the asparagus quickly by placing the pan under running water. This will help to retain its green colour.

Beans and seeds increase in nutritional value when sprouted, and make a good addition to salads and stir frys. You can use most beans, alfalfa or fenugreek seeds, green lentils, wheat or chick peas. Put a few handfuls of washed beans in a large jar. Cover the neck with muslin and fasten with an elastic band. Keep at room temperature (13-22°C 54-70°F). Rinse with fresh water once or twice a day, draining well. In 3 or 4 days the sprouts will be ready.

A classic way to garnish French soups is to serve aïoli sauce on croutons. Make the sauce by adding very finely chopped garlic to mayonnaise, and spread onto small croutons made from sliced and fried French bread. Float in the soup and sprinkle with grated cheese.

If your mayonnaise curdles, it can be easily remedied. Take a clean bowl and put in another egg yolk. Whisk the yolk until it is pale yellow. Then slowly add the curdled mayonnaise mixture, whisking continuously.

Decorate your salads with edible flowers such as lavender, nasturtiums, violets, roses, pansies and pot marigolds as well as the pretty flowers of herbs such as rosemary and thyme.

To prevent avocado mixtures from discolouring, add lemon juice and put the avocado stones back in the dish until you are ready to serve at the table.

For a dainty appetizer, try mixing cream cheese with a strong cheese such as Roquefort or Sage Derby, or just fresh herbs, and pipe onto fingers of cooked puff pastry. Put another layer of pastry on top to form a sandwich.

Oysters look fantastic served on a bed of crushed ice and seaweed. Seaweed is obtainable from good fishmongers. You can also bring a breath of the seashore to the table by putting seaweed around a tureen of fish soup such as Bouillabaisse.

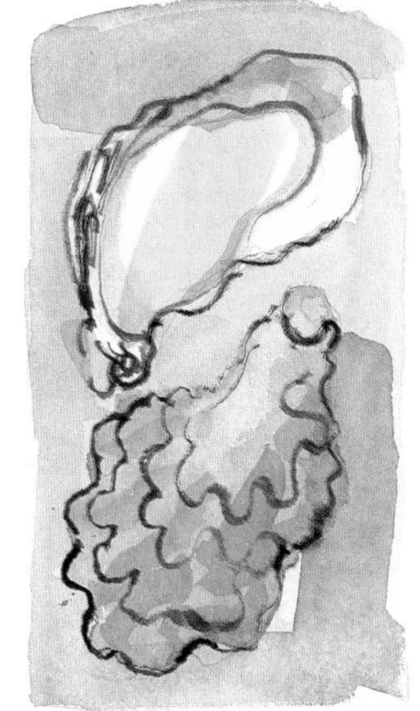

In spring, gather young dandelion leaves for salads. To remove the bitterness, blanch them before picking by placing a flower pot over the growing plants. Mix the leaves with other salad vegetables. Dress with wine vinegar or orange or lemon juice, and wilt by pouring hot olive oil over the leaves. Excellent served with grilled goat's cheese.

In autumn, wild hop shoots can be gathered to make a lovely warm salad. Toss the shoots in oil over a high heat for 2-3 minutes. Dress with the oil from the pan, lemon and chopped hard-boiled eggs. Don't pick hops growing too close to busy roads, as they absorb lead from passing traffic.

The best caviar is Beluga caviar. It contains at least 45 vitamins and minerals per ounce (25 g). As one portion is about two ounces, it makes a very healthy, though expensive, starter. Caviar should be stored at 30°F (−1°C), and never frozen.

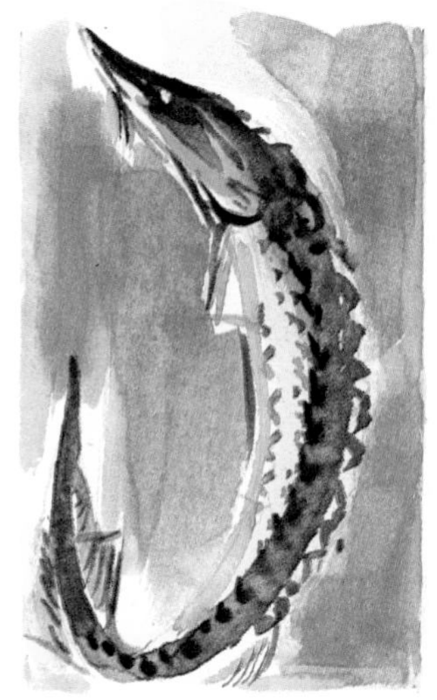

It used to be fashionable to eat caviar with various garnishes, such as chopped onions, eggs, chives, anchovies, sour cream and blini pancakes, but these mask the flavour. True connoisseurs serve caviar on a bed of crushed ice, and eat it with hot toast.

To make a very quick bean pâté, drain a tin of haricot beans and a tin of red kidney beans. Mash with 5oz/125g/$\frac{1}{2}$ cup of curd cheese or *fromage frais*, your favourite herbs, the juice of half an orange, a finely chopped spring onion, salt and pepper. Serve with toast and orange wedges. For a more crunchy texture nuts can also be added. Cooked mung beans make a tasty variation.

Soufflés rise better if the side of the dish has been lightly buttered and floured, or in the case of sweet soufflés, dusted with icing sugar. Adding salt to the egg whites will help them to stay stiff. Resist the temptation to keep peeping inside the oven, or the soufflé will go flat.

Instead of using flour to thicken creamed soups, cook a large chopped potato with the other vegetables. This will make a nice purée when sieved or liquidized.

LIGHT DISHES

Light dishes can be served for supper or lunch, as accompaniments to the main course, or for those who prefer a less heavy meal. If you give your imagination free rein, you can make a selection of dishes complementary to each other which can be just as appetizing as a single main course. This is a good chance to try out interesting taste combinations, and to mix and match food ideas. The permutations are endless.

Use this section to enter many types of dishes which can be treated as meals in their own right, such as soufflés, omelettes, pastas, vegetable dishes, beans and pulses. You can use it also to enter side dishes for curries or main courses, for example vegetables, dressings and sauces. An interesting sauce can transform a simple vegetable into an exquisite dish.

Picnics and barbecues are good at any time of the year. Food tastes so much better in the open air. In winter, make a piping hot stew or bean casserole, and take it with you in a wide-necked vacuum flask on a frosty walk, or serve it on Bonfire Night or Halloween. In summer, take chilled salads and lots of ice in an insulated food bag.

Light dishes can be quickly prepared in an emergency as a separate course or as a side dish. Keep small containers of sauces in the freezer, or mayonnaise and yoghurt in the fridge, to add to tinned and frozen vegetables such as artichokes, peppers or sweet corn.

Raw tomatoes make a light, clean version of tomato sauce for pasta. If prepared in advance, the flavours will have time to permeate. Chop $1\frac{1}{2}$lb/650g skinned tomatoes. Put in a deep bowl, add salt, pepper and 6 leaves of fresh basil, torn to release the flavour. Cover with good quality virgin olive oil, and leave. This sauce also makes a good accompaniment for plain grilled fish.

Sauté cooked slices of potatoes in a dash of walnut oil, and sprinkle with toasted walnuts or hazelnuts.

A quick way to give that Indian flavour to plain cooked rice: gently fry strands of saffron or 1 tablespoon of turmeric in 2 tablespoons of Indian ghee or butter concentrate. Pour over the rice just before serving. Sprinkle with 1 tablespoon of fresh chopped coriander leaves for decoration.

You will save precious vitamins if you avoid boiling leafy vegetables such as spinach or cabbage. Wash spinach removing any coarse stems, and shake off excess water. Put in a large pan with a nob of butter on a high heat and cover tightly. Any moisture left in the leaves will turn to steam. Shake the pan or give a very quick stir once or twice. Shred cabbage finely with a sharp knife, and add a few tablespoons of water or cider, with a chopped apple, to the pan. The vegetables should be cooked in a few minutes.

Vegetables are more delicious and nutritious if cooked very lightly. Grate or finely slice carrots, swedes, turnips or other root vegetables in a food processor. Cook in a covered saucepan with a nob of butter and seasoning for 2-3 minutes, shaking the pan once or twice. If the vegetable is in danger of burning, add a splash of water. Garnish with chopped parsley or crispy bacon for a warming winter dish.

The essence of obtaining an authentic Chinese taste is to use the correct seasonings. For a basic stir fry, heat the pan and add 2 tablespoons of tasteless vegetable oil followed by 1 tablespoon of sesame seed oil. Add 2 small slices of fresh ginger, 1 clove of sliced garlic and 1 chopped spring onion. Fry quickly. Remove the garlic and ginger, and proceed to fry your chosen ingredients.

Boiling sweet corn in salted water tends to make the corn hard, so add the salt after cooking, together with the butter and pepper. Alternatively, roast the corn in its husks over charcoal as they do in the Caribbean.

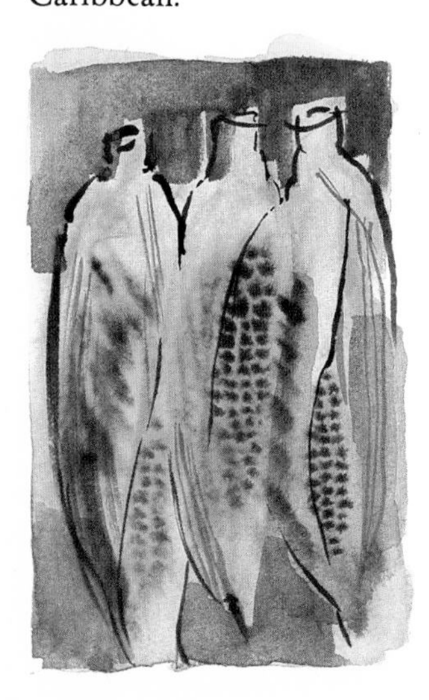

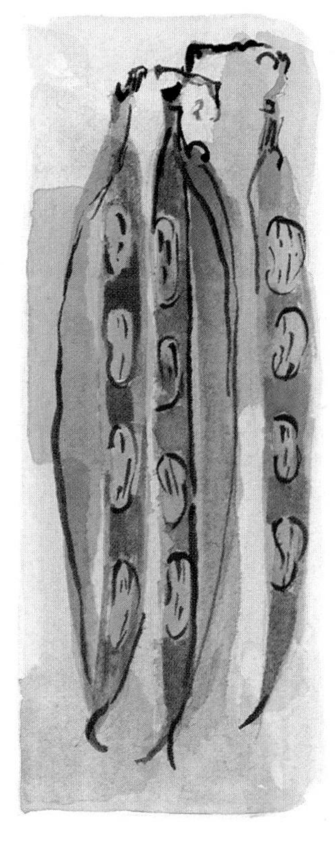

If at the end of the runner or green bean season you are left with some stringy beans, do not throw them on the compost heap. Use the beans inside the pod to add to French and Italian peasant stews.

If you forget to soak dried beans over night, put them in a pan and cover with boiling water. Allow to stand for one hour, and then cook for the normal length of time.

To peel tomatoes, make a small cross with a sharp knife at the bottom of the tomato. Plunge into boiling water for 5 seconds and then immediately plunge into a bowl under running cold water. You will now find that the skin can be peeled away quite easily.

For a superb risotto try to use Italian Arborio rice. You need 4oz/100g/1 cup of rice to $\frac{3}{4}$pt/450ml/2 cups of stock per person. Coat the rice well in butter or oil in a heavy saucepan over a moderate heat. Add the hot stock, a ladleful at a time, stirring continuously with a wooden spoon. Do not add more liquid until it has all been absorbed. The key to success is not to add too much stock too quickly. Cook until the rice is just *al dente*, creamy and moist. Add your choice of cheese, fish or vegetables at this stage, and garnish with chopped herbs.

For a simple and classic finish to fresh ravioli, melt 8oz/200g/1 cup of butter and add about 15 chopped leaves of fresh sage. Stew for a few minutes without browning the butter. Serve the sauce separately in a jug or sauceboat.

The South Americans have a way of cooking fish without heat. They marinade fresh chopped fish in lemon or lime juice, finely sliced onion and crushed garlic for at least 3 hours. The fish turns milky white, and it will keep well for 3 days. Dress this dish with cubed avocados.

To make a salad dressing to accompany grated raw root vegetables, crumble two hard-boiled egg yolks into a bowl and gradually beat in $\frac{1}{2}$pt/300ml/1$\frac{1}{4}$ cups of olive oil, 1 tablespoon of lemon juice, chopped parsley and a crushed clove of garlic.

Pitta bread makes good pouches for sandwich fillings. To make a pouch, heat bread under the grill, and when hot and slightly puffy, slit open with a knife. Leave to cool, and then put in your favourite fillings.

For a Spanish-style picnic, try a potato omelette or tortilla. This is just as delicious cold as hot. Make the omelette very thick and pack it into the picnic basket with salads. For a cooling element on a hot steamy day, start the picnic with gazpacho poured over frozen tomato juice cubes from the vacuum flask.

For a poor man's version of champagne and smoked salmon at a summer picnic, try serving pink champagne with a pink smoked mackerel pâté. To make the pâté, remove the skin and any bones from the fish, mash the flesh and mix with cream, *crème fraîche*, or curd cheese. Add lemon juice and chopped hard-boiled egg, and decorate with pink pepper corns. Serve with corn chips and crudités.

MAIN COURSES

Theme meals can be amusing and full of surprises, and the best place to start designing such a meal is with the main course. They provide plenty of scope for your creative gifts. Why not hold a black and white (or any other colour combination) dinner, base a meal on a foreign country, a historical period, or celebrate an event such as an election? Plan the whole concept, the costume and table decoration as well as the food. Consider reviving traditional festivals such as Michaelmas, when you can cook a goose as a centrepiece and decorate the table with Michaelmas daisies. In other words, use any excuse for a special meal!

When planning your menu, always think about what you will eat before and after the main course so that you have a variety of textures. If you start with soup, do not serve a stew next, since it offers too much liquid – a drier main course would be more acceptable. Bearing this in mind, aim for contrasts with the other courses, for instance moist with dry, and heavy with light. The same applies to vegetarian cooking, since balance is very important.

As well as special dishes, remember to include in your collection recipes which are suitable for your everyday lifestyle. It is possible to produce tasty food simply and economically. For example, cheaper cuts of meat become more interesting by making a marinade from a variety of oriental spices. Whether you are cooking for a large family or just for yourself, you might like to experiment with various types of one-pot meals such as laksa from Malaysia and pot-au-feu from France. These practical dishes can be prepared in advance and dipped into at different times.

Insert pieces of Parma ham with sprigs of rosemary into slashes made in a leg of lamb. This will give a flavour evocative of sheep bred on salt marshes where they have grazed on aromatic herbs. Good with roast chicken too. Parma ham is also delicious in saltimbocca or when used to roll up beef olives.

Fish such as salmon, red mullet and salmon trout go very well with chilled red wines. In fact most oily fish and shell fish cooked in a dark sauce can be served with low tannin red wines which do not interfere with the flavour of the fish.

Fresh summer savory is a somewhat peppery herb which makes a good substitute for ground pepper. It goes well with beans, cheese and stuffings for roast meat.

Cassoulets are very easy to prepare and can be made with whatever is in season and to hand. Always include partially cooked beans, placed in layers between 2 or 3 different types of meat together with seasoning and vegetables. Cook slowly in the oven for 2-3 hours, periodically breaking the crust that forms, and stirring it into the mixture.

A delicious eastern marinade for chicken or lamb kebabs: mix a small carton of yoghurt with 2 tablespoons of chopped mint, the juice of a lemon, 1 clove of garlic and 1 tablespoon each of olive oil, paprika, ground coriander, ground cumin and chilli powder. Marinate for at least 12 hours before grilling or barbecuing.

Marinades are an aromatic way of flavouring and tenderizing game casseroles or roasts. Take 1 pt/ 600ml/2½ cups of red wine, a dash of vinegar and ¼pt/150ml/⅔ cup of water, a chopped onion, mixed herbs including bayleaf, juniper berries, and black peppercorns. Marinate meat for at least 24 hours, turning once or twice so that all the flavours are absorbed. If roasting, add the marinade to the pan after cooking and reduce to make the gravy.

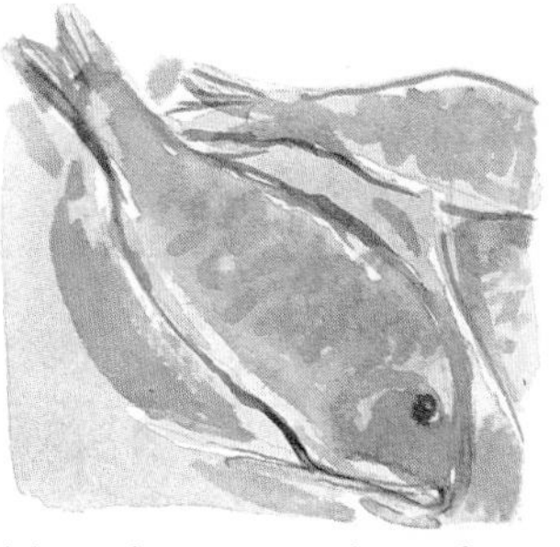

Try salt crust cooking for a change. It seals in all the pure flavours and is delicious for chicken or fish such as sea bass or red mullet. Use about 2lb/1kg/ 4 cups of coarse grained sea salt. Line a cast iron oven dish with a third of the salt. Lay in the chicken or fish and cover with the remaining salt. Sprinkle with a little water and bake the chicken for 20 minutes and the fish for 15 minutes per pound/500g at 200°C/ 400°F/Gas mark 6. Take the dish to the table and break the salt crust.

Cream cheese mixed with some fresh breadcrumbs makes a delicate stuffing base for veal escolopes or flattened chicken breasts. Roll the meat round the stuffing and secure with cocktail sticks. Then sauté or pot roast.

Use cooked rice instead of breadcrumbs for stuffing chicken, lamb or pork. Mix into the rice grated zest and juice of an orange or lemon, your favourite herbs and some diced dried fruit such as apricots or pears. Roast in the usual way, and add some more zest to the sauce in the pan.

Curry dishes taste better if kept in the fridge for a few days to allow the spicy flavour to develop. Grind fresh spices yourself to obtain the best results. Frying or dry roasting the spices before making a curry also helps to enrich the flavour and to release the oils.

Filo pastry is classically used for Greek confections, but it makes an excellent pastry for savouries. It comes in ultra fine sheets, and is very useful to have in the freezer, being easily refrozen. There is no mess with flour, and you are assured of a crisp, light and flaky pastry every time. Use up to 5 layers with melted butter in between. Place filling in the middle of the top layer, and fold or roll. Fill with poached fish in a light sauce or cooked vegetables and grated cheese.

It is great fun to try the paperbag or *en papillote* method of cooking low fat foods such as fish, chicken or vegetables. Butter a sheet of greaseproof paper or foil large enough to fold round the food. Make a parcel, seal by turning over the edges several times, and then bake. The bag will puff up like a pillow if it is well sealed, keeping in all the flavours and juices. When cooked, open with scissors and serve on a dish in the bag.

Chick peas are a useful way of making meat go further. They must be soaked and cooked first. As the peas are very bland, they need garlic, lemon juice and olive oil to improve their flavour, for instance in chicken and lamb stews. Add handfuls of spinach, and garnish with coriander to give them a true Middle Eastern flavour.

If you need coconut milk for an Indonesian or Malaysian curry, place 3oz/75g/$\frac{3}{4}$ cup of dessicated cocunut in a saucepan and cover with $\frac{1}{4}$pt/150ml/$\frac{2}{3}$ cup of water. Bring to the boil and then remove from the heat. Leave covered, and when cold press the juice through a sieve. You can make a thinner milk by repeating the process several times. Suitable also for adding to soups and puddings.

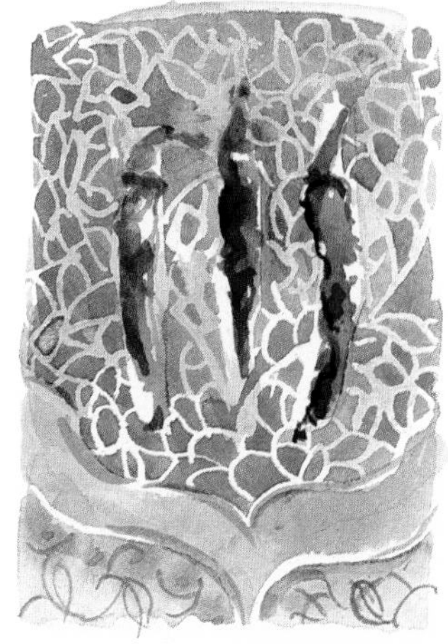

There are various ways to glaze ham which you have boiled in stock with added orange juice or cider. For a honey glaze, remove the skin from the ham or bacon, brush on melted honey (in France they add a little mustard) and stick with cloves. Put into a hot oven for 20-25 minutes.

For a breadcrumb finish, remove the skin, sprinkle with breadcrumbs, the zest of an orange and your favourite herb, and brown under the grill.

To achieve perfectly thin slices of beef for Japanese sukiyaki or pork for stir frying, pop it in the freezer for a few hours to firm up the flesh (it should not become rock hard). Cut against the grain, using a sharp knife. Useful for smoked salmon too.

To give boiled beef a really spicy Eastern taste, take $\frac{1}{2}$ teaspoon each of ground cinnamon, star anise, cloves, Szechuan pepper corns, and fry for a few minutes before adding the joint and the stock. Cook in the usual way, and serve sliced with some of the liquid poured over. Delicious hot or cold.

Instead of making apple sauce as an accompaniment to roast pork, core and fill whole or halved dessert apples with dried apricots and bake in the roasting pan. The apples help to make a colourful dish.

DESSERTS

Desserts may be very elaborate or the most simple course of all. A ripe pear, served on a pretty plate, can be the perfect end to a meal – simplicity itself. Alternatively, be extravagant and serve an elaborate and fanciful creation with mountains of cream, making sure that the other courses are very light. Sometimes try a savoury or a selection of interesting cheeses instead.

Desserts offer a splendid opportunity to indulge your fantasies. Make a note in this section of as many different ideas as possible. With a bit of practice, piping whipped cream becomes easy and helps to inspire that element of delight and surprise among your friends at the end of the meal. For dramatic effects, flamber desserts, and on Pancake Day why not make crêpes suzettes? Use edible flowers such as roses and violets for decoration, or chocolate leaves which are easily made by painting the top side of rose leaves with melted chocolate. You could also experiment with flowers in the desserts themselves, as in marigold cheesecake or elderflower fritters.

Sauces made from puréed fruits and sweetened with sugar or honey and perhaps a drop or two of liqueur are good to pour over ice creams and sorbets. Try out interesting contrasts such as a sharp sauce with a sweet dessert, or maybe serve a crunchy sweet biscuit such as shortbread or brandy snaps to set off the softness of cold soufflés and mousses. Nowadays we are more weight conscious and there are fewer people with the traditional sweet tooth, so serve *crème fraîche* or strained Greek yoghurt instead of cream, and place sugar on the table instead of adding too much to the recipe.

To give strawberries that special velvety touch, squeeze fresh orange or lime juice over the fruit and add a dash of Grand Marnier. Serve with delicate dessert biscuits instead of cream.

A pretty way to present sorbets, desserts or cocktails served in glass goblets: frost individual glass dishes by moistening the rims with a wedge of orange or lemon and then dip into caster or icing sugar. Chill before filling with your favourite sorbet or ice cream.

To make brandy snap baskets for filling with ice cream or sorbets, gently warm shop-bought brandy snaps in a medium oven. When they are soft, unroll and carefully shape on upturned cups. Leave to cool. Make sure that the bases of the baskets are flat or they will tip over.

If you want to serve pancakes to a lot of people, make a stack of them, and fill each layer with fruit and cream, rather like a cake. Cream cheese with crispy bacon makes a tasty savoury filling.

A little jam and water, heated until boiling and then strained, makes a lovely glaze for fruit tarts and flans, especially the classic French apple tart.

An ice cream recipe for an emergency: whip $\frac{1}{2}$pt/ 300ml/1$\frac{1}{4}$ cups of double cream until stiff. Fold in a jar of jam – apricot, blackcurrant, raspberry, black cherry or ginger marmalade – and freeze in individual pots for $\frac{3}{4}$ hour. Transfer to the fridge 10-15 minutes before serving. Melt chocolate in a pan over hot water and pour over the ice cream. The coldness of the ice cream will cause the chocolate to set almost immediately.

Dried fruit such as prunes, pears, Hunza apricots and apples make a really special winter compôte if marinated in weak black tea before cooking and finished with a drop of brandy. Serve with plain ice cream and plenty of juice poured over.

Use leftover egg yolks for profiteroles, hollandaise sauce or mayonnaise. You can also enrich pastry with an egg yolk, thicken stewed fruit, or whisk into sauces or soups (always add yolks off the heat).

Use leftover egg whites to make meringues. Fold whipped whites into an omelette mixture to make a soufflé omelette and fill with strawberries or raspberries and cream. Home made nougat and royal icing are also good ways to use up egg whites. Add a pinch of salt to whites that are to be stiffly beaten. The older the egg, the more bulky it will become when whipped.

Cooked damsons are particularly delicious served with a very sharp lemon ice cream or rich chocolate ice cream or mousse.

To make vanilla sugar, fill a jar with caster sugar and insert a vanilla pod. The flavour will last a year, and you can keep it topped up with fresh sugar. Use dried orange or lemon peel in the same way.

Elegant chocolate curls will make any dessert look special, and are easy to make. Melt a good quantity of chocolate and spread thickly onto a marble slab to cool. When completely set, shave flakes of chocolate by drawing a sharp knife slowly and firmly across the chocolate. Use the flakes immediately.

Sweet cicely enhances whipped cream and any type of milk-based pudding that needs just a little sweetening. Nutmeg also adds sweetness and brings out the creaminess of milk dishes, helping to reduce sugar intake.

To make cream lighter and go further, whip $\frac{1}{2}$pt/300ml/1$\frac{1}{4}$ cups of double cream with a teaspoon of sugar and fold into a stiffly beaten egg white.

Decorate your cheeseboard according to the type of cheese you are eating. Use fresh vine leaves, fig leaves and fresh figs with soft and continental cheeses.

For a more English cheese-board use raspberry or hop leaves with a few old fashioned apples such as Discovery or Russets, or else with Conference pears.

OTHER DISHES

Use this section for notes which have not fitted in elsewhere – breakfasts, teas, preserved fruit and vegetables, drinks and a store cupboard list.

Depending on your style of breakfast, you can note muesli recipes, American pancakes and muffins, classical English devilled kidneys, kedgeree, or even Japanese miso soup with a raw or lightly poached egg.

Tea is a meal to be taken at your leisure, whether you are having afternoon tea on the lawn with cucumber sandwiches and sponge cakes, or a hearty farmhouse tea with cold meats, pies, scones and fruit cakes. Recipes for light cakes and biscuits to be served with morning coffee or your nightcap always come in useful.

From the summer glut of fruit and vegetables make jams and preserves, relishes and pickles, and gather wild fruits and herbs for your store cupboard. Collect recipes for a variety of drinks, anything from home made drinking chocolate for a special Sunday breakfast to mulled wine for a winter party.

Make a lovely jam using wild fruit such as elderberries, which taste like a combination of blackcurrants and blackberries. As they contain a lot of pips, sieve the jam before packing into jars. This makes a good topping for cheesecakes or warm it up as a fruit sauce for ice cream.

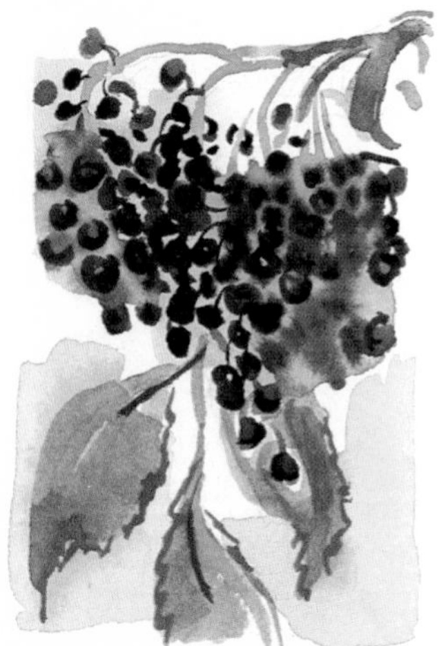

To toast nuts, spread flaked almonds or hazel nuts onto a flat baking tray, and place under a hot grill for a few minutes. Watch them continuously and stir to prevent them from burning. Leave to cool, and then store in an airtight jar. Use sprinkled over vegetables or desserts.

To obtain more juice from lemons, soak them in hot water for about 5 minutes, then cut in half and squeeze as usual.

To remove the bitter taste and waxy surface from lemon peel, blanch in a saucepan of boiling water for 2 minutes and then drain. You can do the same with all citrus fruits.

A good way to keep fresh herbs at their best for the winter is to mix them with butter. Roll the mixture in foil, twist the ends and store in the freezer. Cut off the quantity you require and use the butter for cooking.

Herbs added to cooking oil preserve their taste for the winter. Basil oil is particularly good. Pour oil over the leaves in a glass jar and store. You can add dried chillis to oil in the same way, and use to spice up tomato-based dishes.

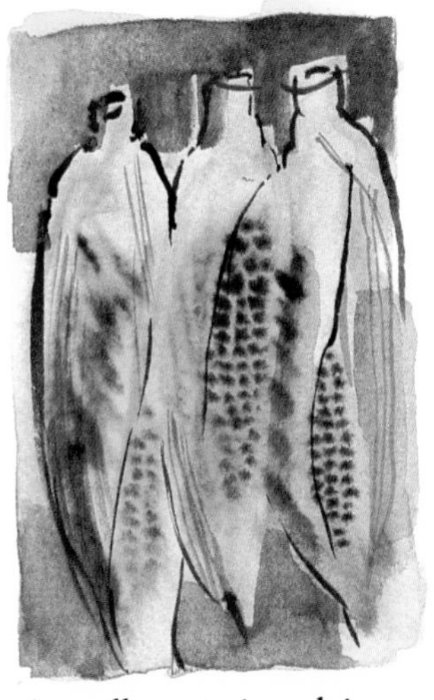

As well as putting plain black pepper on the table, fill another grinder with equal quantities of Szechuan pepper, green and white pepper corns and some allspice. Delicious ground over sweet corn, and over a chicken before roasting.

For a delicious lemon topping to a plain sponge cake, mix the juice of a lemon with 2 tablespoons of icing sugar, and stir until dissolved. Prick the warm cake all over while still in the tin, and pour the lemon mixture slowly over the cake. When cold, remove from the tin. If you want a stronger taste, add the zest of the lemon to the cake mixture before baking.

Before pouring runny fillings into a pastry case, seal the case using an egg yolk, an egg white or a beaten egg. Brush the inside of the case after it has been baked blind and return to the oven for a few minutes to seal and dry. When cool, add the filling.

Herb vinegars are very simple to make. Place a few sprigs of your chosen herb into a bottle of cider or white wine vinegar. Screw on the cap, and leave to mature for about 3 weeks.

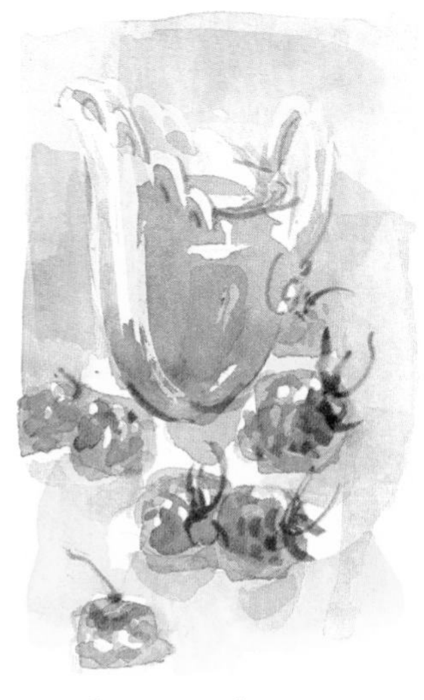

Raspberries make an excellent vinegar for salad dressing. Take 1lb/500g of fresh fruit to $\frac{1}{2}$pt/300ml/ $1\frac{1}{4}$ cups wine vinegar. Pour into a glass jar with a well-fitting lid, and keep on a sunny window sill for a few weeks. Shake daily and strain through a sieve or muslin before bottling. Can be frozen in a suitable container.

Try making an original chutney with plums, pumpkins or gooseberries. These relishes make an excellent complement to cold venison or wild boar. They can be made in the same way as the more usual chutneys, by cooking the fruit until soft in wine vinegar, spices and a little sugar. When cool, pack into jars and store for 4-5 weeks before opening. This allows the flavour to mature properly.

Make lassi as they do in India from yoghurt and crushed ice, and dilute with a little water. Add salt (or sugar for a sweet version) to taste, and whizz in the liquidizer. Garnish with cucumber (or fruit for the sweet drink).

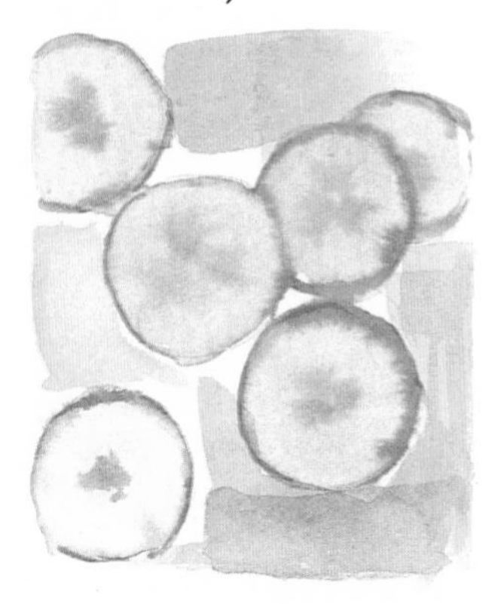

Iced coffee and tea are excellent for quenching the thirst on hot summer days. For something special, crush a handful of ripe strawberries or raspberries with a little sugar, and top up with orange juice, soda water and a squeeze of lime juice. More exotic fruits like mangoes make excellent summer drinks too. Garnish with a sprig of mint or a few slices of orange.

WINE NOTES

Wine	*Year & Region*	*Comments*

Wine	*Year & Region*	*Comments*

BASIC RECIPES

Mayonnaise

Almost anything can be added to mayonnaise to vary it according to what you are eating. It is the basis of many different sauces eaten with cold dishes and salads.

$\frac{1}{4}$pt/150ml/$\frac{2}{3}$ cup tasteless oil
1 teaspoon vinegar or lemon juice
1 egg yolk
salt and pepper
pinch of English mustard powder

Whisk the yolk, vinegar, salt and pepper until they become pale in colour. Very slowly pour in a thick stream of oil whilst whisking continuously until all the oil is used up. Adjust the seasoning. If the mayonnaise is too thick, a little water or vinegar may be added. For a really light mayonnaise gently fold in a stiffly beaten eggwhite.

Variations

Green Sauce
Add 2oz/50g herbs such as spinach, tarragon, chervil, parsley or watercress.

Tartare Sauce
Add 1oz/25g capers, 2oz/50g gherkins, 1oz/25g chopped parsley, and/or chopped hard-boiled egg, and/or chopped green olives.

Mustard Sauce
Add 1 tablespoon each of Dijon mustard and dill weed.

Hollandaise Sauce

This classic warm butter sauce is excellent with fish, eggs and vegetables. For a variation, you can mix in fresh chopped herbs. The addition of a tablespoon of hollandaise sauce to a basic white sauce will help it to glaze well under the grill.

6oz/150g/$\frac{3}{4}$ cup butter
2 egg yolks
salt
6 crushed pepper corns
1 tablespoon vinegar
2 tablespoons water

Reduce the vinegar, water and peppercorns in a saucepan until 1 tablespoon of liquid remains. Strain off the pepper corns and allow to cool. Whisk the vinegar and the egg yolks in a bowl over a pan of hot water on a medium heat until they thicken to the consistency of cream. Remove from the heat and cool. Meanwhile melt the butter gently and when the egg yolks have cooled, gradually whisk in the butter, in the same way as you make mayonnaise. Adjust the seasoning.

White Sauce

This is the classic white sauce used in dishes such as lasagne, English fish pie, and as the basis for parsley sauce and mornay sauce. It can be finished with an egg yolk and a few tablespoons of cream at the last minute or just before serving. Do this when the sauce is off the heat or it will curdle, and do not return to the heat.

1pt/600ml/2½ cups milk
2oz/50g/4 tablespoons margarine/butter
2oz/50g/½ cup flour

Melt the margarine/butter slowly in a saucepan over a gentle heat. Stir in the flour with a wooden spoon until the mixture binds together and is very smooth. This is called a roux. Gradually add warmed milk, stirring well. If any lumps form, beat them out or pass the sauce through a sieve before adding any more milk. Simmer gently for a minimum of 10 minutes. The longer you cook it, the less floury the sauce will taste. You can freeze it in small containers.

Variations

Vegetable dishes:
Use a milk base. Add cheese, hard-boiled eggs or herbs.

Chicken dishes:
Use chicken stock. Add 3oz/75g sliced mushrooms or herbs.

Fish dishes:
Use fish stock. Add 2oz/50g/½ cup cheese, or hard-boiled eggs with a dash of anchovy essence, or herbs, or cooked onion.

Basic Tomato Sauce

This is the best known of Italian sauces, but not the oldest. Tomatoes came to Italy from America at the time of the Renaissance, but were not commonly eaten until the eighteenth century. Use this sauce for all types of pasta dishes as well as with fish, meat and vegetable dishes. Make three times this quantity of sauce and freeze what you do not use in small containers, to enrich soups and stews.

2 chopped onions
1 14oz/397g tin tomatoes
olive oil
herbs (such as basil and bayleaf)
a few drops chilli oil (optional)
crushed garlic (optional)

Gently cook the garlic and onions in the oil until transparent. Add the herbs and cook for a few minutes. Add the tomatoes and bring to the boil, breaking them down with a wooden spoon. Simmer gently for 15-30 minutes or longer if you want a thick sauce. Add the chilli oil and seasoning to taste.

Batter

This is a light frying batter which is good for delicate foods like Japanese tempura. Borage, marjoram, nasturtium or courgette flowers are excellent cooked in this batter. If you prefer a sweet batter for apples, bananas or even the borage flowers, replace the Parmesan with the zest of half an orange, and serve sprinkled with sugar and lemon or orange juice.

1 egg separated
1 tablespoon water
1 tablespoon oil
pinch salt
zest of 1 lemon
3oz/75g/¾ cup sifted flour
1 tablespoon grated Parmesan cheese
oil for deep frying

Beat the egg yolk with the water, oil, salt and lemon zest until well blended. Add the sifted flour and cheese, and stir. Leave to stand for 1½ hours. Beat the egg whites until they form stiff peaks, and fold them gently into the batter with a metal spoon. Dip your chosen food and fry immediately in hot deep fat.

Basic Pasta

Pasta can be made into almost any shape and is very versatile. By adding a few simple ingredients to the basic pasta, you can create a wide variety of dishes. Use fish, meat or vegetables, according to your mood. There are many different sauces which go well with pasta. For the best results, use pure semolina flour.

8oz/200g/2 cups flour
2 large eggs
pinch salt
1 tablespoon olive oil (optional – it will make a softer dough)

Sieve the flour and salt, and make a well in the centre. Mix in the eggs and oil, adding a little water if it is too dry to bind together, or more flour if it is too wet. Knead for 10 minutes by hand or put through a pasta machine. Place in the fridge in a plastic bag for 25 minutes before rolling out and cutting into the shapes you require.

Shortcrust Pastry

When making pastry, it is important to remember to use a cool liquid, handle the dough as little as possible, and roll out the pastry evenly. If you are making a tart with a runny filling, you need to bake the pastry blind to stop it becoming soggy. Line the flan tin with the pastry, cover with a sheet of greaseproof paper, and then put in a handful of dried beans. The weight of the beans helps to stop the pastry from bubbling up unevenly. Bake at 200°C/400°F/Gas mark 6 for about 10 minutes. Remove the paper and beans, and put the pastry back in the oven for a few minutes to dry out before filling.

5oz/125g/1¼ cup plain flour
2oz/50g/4 tablespoons each of butter and lard or white vegetable fat
pinch salt
1 tablespoon lemon juice, and water

Sieve the flour and salt into a large bowl. Grate the butter and lard and quickly rub into the flour until the mixture resembles fine breadcrumbs. Add the lemon juice and use enough water to bind the dough together. Set aside and leave to rest for at least 20 minutes before rolling out.

Variations
Savoury pastry:
Add herbs and grated cheese.
Sweet pastry:
Add a little sugar or grated orange zest.

Puff Pastry

This is the finest of all pastries. There are few things more satisfying than seeing this pastry rise, and with it you can achieve some gorgeous-looking desserts. Use it for millefeuilles, cream slices, meat or fish pies, vols-au-vents and other savouries.

8oz/200g/2 cups plain flour
8oz/200g/2 cups butter
lemon juice and water
salt

Sieve the flour and salt together in a bowl and rub in 1oz/25g/2 tablespoons of the butter. Gently combine using the water and a squeeze of lemon juice to form a soft dough. Set aside the pastry to rest for 30 minutes. Roll out into an oblong shape, and roll the butter into the same shape half the size of the dough. Place the butter at one end of the dough. Fold the dough over the butter, and press the edges down. Carefully roll out to its original size and fold into three, making an oblong. Rest for 20 minutes. Roll out again, with the narrow ends facing towards you. Fold again, and repeat the process of resting, rolling out and folding 6 more times.

Bread Dough

Use this dough for making buns as well as bread. An extra tablespoon of olive oil makes it into a good pizza dough.

1lb/400gm/4 cups strong bread flour
1oz/25g/2 tablespoons fat – margarine/butter/lard/olive oil
½oz/12g fresh yeast or one sachet dried yeast
½pt/300ml/1¼ cups warm water or half quantities milk and water
½ teaspoon sugar, pinch salt

Sieve the flour and salt into a warm bowl. Dissolve the yeast and sugar with a quarter of the liquid. Make a well in the centre of the flour and pour in the yeast mixture. Sprinkle a little flour over the top. Cover with a cloth and leave in a warm place to ferment. When the yeast bubbles, add the rest of the liquid and fat kneading together to form a smooth dough. Leave covered with a damp cloth in a warm place until risen to at least twice the original size. Knead again and make into a loaf, buns or pizza. Cover and put in a warm place until it has doubled in size again and then bake in a hot oven.

Choux Pastry

This is very easy to make, but it is worth taking care with beating the mixture so that it will rise really well and leave a hollow large enough for a savoury or sweet filling. Why not make a *croquenbouche* from a mountain of profiteroles as a celebration centrepiece?

5oz/125g/1¼ cups flour
4oz/100g/½ cup butter
½pt/300ml/1¼ cups water
pinch salt and pinch sugar
4 eggs, lightly beaten

In a heavy pan bring the water, sugar and butter to the boil. Remove from the heat and sieve in the flour and salt, and beat with a wooden spoon. Return to a medium heat, beating continuously until all the lumps have gone and the mixture starts to leave the sides of the pan. Remove from the heat and beat the eggs slowly into the mixture, which should have a dropping consistency. Place the paste into a piping bag with a 1 inch/2cm nozzle, and pipe small pieces the size of a walnut onto a lightly greased baking sheet. For eclairs pipe 3 inch/6cm lengths, and for savoury buns pipe small pieces slightly smaller than a walnut. Bake for 25-30 minutes, depending on the size, at 220°C/425°F/Gas mark 7. Allow to cool before filling.

Victoria Sponge

This is a basic sponge mix which makes a beautifully light cake to which you could add grated zest of citrus fruit, dessicated coconut or cocoa power. Make fillings with butter cream, fresh cream or your own home-made jam. Decorate the cake in any way you please. The simplest idea is to place a paper doyly over the top, lightly sprinkle with icing sugar, and then carefully remove the doyly.

4oz/100g/½cup margarine/butter
4oz/100g/½ cup caster sugar
4oz/100g/1 cup self-raising flour
2 large eggs, beaten

In a large bowl cream the sugar and softened margarine/butter until pale yellow and fluffy. Stir in the eggs a little at a time. Sieve the flour and gently fold into the mixture until it has all been incorporated. Place in two 7inch/18cm greased sandwich tins, and bake at 350°F/180°C/Gas mark 4 for 25-30 minutes. Remove from the oven, cool for a few minutes and turn out onto a rack. When cool, decorate and fill. For the chocolate version, substitute 1oz/25g/¼ cup of cocoa powder for 1oz/25g/¼ cup flour.

Fruit Cake

This is a medium rich cake which will keep well and mature. If you prefer a somewhat moister cake, soak the fruit in a little strong tea for about ½ hour. Strain before adding to the cake mixture.

8oz/200g/2 cups flour
5oz/125g/⅝ cup butter/margarine
3oz/75g/¾ cup each of chopped glacé cherries and chopped peel
2 large or 3 small eggs, beaten
5oz/125g/⅝ cup caster sugar
4oz/100g/1 cup each of currants and sultanas
2oz/50g/½ cup almonds
½ teaspoon mixed spice

Cream the fat and sugar until soft and fluffy. Gradually add the eggs. Sieve the flour and gently fold into the mixture. Then add the rest of the ingredients except the almonds. Pour the mixture into a 7 inch/18cm cake tin, greased and lined with paper. Place the almonds on top and bake at 150°C/300°F/Gas mark 2 for ¾ hour, then reduce the temperature to 120°C/240°F/Gas mark ½. Cover with paper and cook for a further 1¼ hours.

HERB CHART

	Stocks, Soups and Sauces	Vegetable Dishes	Savoury Grains and Pasta	Pulses and Beans	Egg and Dairy	Fish	Meat	Poultry and Game	Sweet Dishes and Puddings	Baking and Jams	Pickles, Chutneys Preserves, Vinegars	Drinks, Sweet and Savoury
Allspice	○	○				○	○	○			○	○
Angelica									○	○		
Aniseed		○					○	○	○	○		○
Basil	○	○	○	○	○	○	○	○	○			
Balm		○	○	○		○	○	○	○			
Bay	○	○	○	○	○	○	○	○	○			
Bergamot					○							○
Borage	○	○	○			○			○	○	○	○
Caraway seed	○	○	○	○	○		○			○		○
Cardomon	○	○	○	○	○	○	○	○			○	
Cayenne	○	○	○	○	○	○	○	○			○	
Celery seed	○	○	○	○	○	○	○	○				○
Chervil	○	○	○	○	○	○	○	○				
Chilli	○	○	○	○	○	○	○	○				○
Chives	○	○	○	○	○	○	○	○				○
Cinnamon								○	○	○	○	○
Cloves	○										○	
Coriander seed	○	○	○	○	○		○		○	○	○	
leaf	○	○	○	○	○	○	○	○				
Cumin	○	○		○	○	○	○				○	
Curry powder	○	○	○	○	○	○	○	○			○	
Dill	○	○	○	○	○	○	○	○			○	○
Fennel	○	○		○	○	○	○	○			○	
Fenugreek		○	○	○	○	○	○	○			○	
Garlic	○	○	○	○	○	○	○	○			○	
Ginger powder	○						○	○	○	○	○	○
Horseradish						○	○	○			○	

	Stocks, Soups and Sauces	Vegetable Dishes	Savoury Grains and Pasta	Pulses and Beans	Egg and Dairy	Fish	Meat	Poultry and Game	Sweet Dishes and Puddings	Baking and Jams	Pickles, Chutneys Preserves, Vinegars	Drinks, Sweet and Savoury
Juniper	O	O				O	O	O			O	O
Lemon grass	O	O		O		O	O	O	O		O	
Lovage	O	O	O	O	O	O	O	O			O	O
Mace	O	O		O	O	O	O	O	O		O	
Marjoram	O	O	O	O	O	O	O	O			O	O
Mint	O	O	O	O	O	O	O	O	O		O	O
Mustard	O	O	O	O	O	O	O	O			O	
Nutmeg	O	O	O	O	O		O	O	O	O	O	O
Oregano	O	O	O	O	O	O	O	O			O	O
Paprika	O	O	O	O	O	O	O	O			O	O
Parsley	O	O	O	O	O	O	O	O			O	O
Pepper corns	O	O	O	O	O	O	O	O			O	O
Poppyseeds									O	O		
Rosemary	O	O	O	O	O	O	O	O				O
Saffron	O	O	O	O	O	O	O	O	O	O	O	O
Sage	O	O	O	O	O		O	O			O	O
Savory	O	O	O	O	O	O	O	O				O
Sorrel	O		O	O	O	O	O	O				
Shallots	O	O	O	O		O	O	O			O	
Star anise							O				O	
Sweet cicely	O	O					O			O		O
Tamarind	O	O	O	O		O	O	O			O	O
Tansy	O	O				O			O			O
Tarragon	O	O	O	O	O	O	O	O			O	O
Thyme	O	O	O	O	O	O	O	O				O
Thyme lemon	O	O	O	O	O	O	O	O				O
Turmeric	O	O	O	O		O	O	O			O	

COOKERY CHARTS

Note: when following the weights and measures in recipes, use either the imperial or the metric scale. Never mix them up, as the amounts given may be equivalents, and not exact measures. American, Canadian and New Zealand weights and measures are all the same, but Australian weights and measures are approximately ten per cent greater.

IMPERIAL – METRIC COMPARISONS

DRY WEIGHTS

Imperial	Metric approx equivalent	Metric exact equivalent
¼oz	5g	7.0g
½oz	10g	14.1g
1oz	25g	28.3g
2oz	50g	56.6g
3oz	75g	84.9g
4oz	100g	113.2g
8oz	200g	227.0g
12oz	300g	340.0g
16oz (1lb)	400g	454.0g
2lb	1kg	898.0g

LIQUIDS

Imperial	Metric approx equivalent	Metric exact equivalent
¼pt/5 fluid oz	125ml	142ml
½pt/10 fluid oz	250ml/¼ litre	284ml
¾pt/15 fluid oz	375ml	426ml
1pt/20 fluid oz	500ml/½ litre	568ml
1½pt/30 fluid oz	750ml/¾ litre	852ml
2pt/1qt	1000ml/1 litre	1.13 litre
2qt	2000ml/2 litre	2.26 litre
1 gal	4½ litre	4.54 litre

IMPERIAL – AMERICAN COMPARISONS

DRY WEIGHTS

Imperial	American
8oz fat	1 cup
4oz flour	1 cup
8oz sugar	1 cup
4½oz icing sugar	1 cup
12oz syrup or treacle	1 cup
7oz rice and grains	1 cup
5oz dried fruit	1 cup
2oz fresh breadcrumbs	1 cup
4oz chopped nuts	1 cup

LIQUIDS

Imperial	American
2 tablespoons	3 tablespoons
3 tablespoons	¼ cup
¼ pint	⅔ cup
½ pint	1¼ cups
¾ pint	just 2 cups
1 pint	2½ cups

OVEN TEMPERATURES

Dishes	C°	F°	Gas no.	Temperature
Meringues, drying bread	100	225	¼	very cool
Bottling fruit	130	250	½	very cool
Egg dishes and custards, milk puddings, baked fish	140	275	1	cool
Stews, rich fruit cakes, baked fruit	150	300	2	slow
Casseroles, slow roasting, braised meat and vegetables, plain fruit cakes	170	325	3	moderately slow
Madeira cake, Victoria sponge	180	350	4	moderate
Biscuits, whisked sponges, small cakes	190	375	5	moderately hot
Shortcrust pastry, tarts	200	400	6	hot
Fast roasting, scones, bread, choux pastry	220	425	7	very hot
Soufflés, puff and flaky pastry, pilafs, roast potatoes, yeast buns, rolls.	230	450	8	very fast

ROASTING TIMES

Meat	Time per lb	Extra time	Temperature
Lamb	20 mins	+20 mins	450°-475°F: pink
Beef	15 mins	+15 mins	450°-475°F: rare
Pork	25 mins	+25 mins	450°-475°F: well done
Veal	25 mins	+25 mins	450°-475°F: well done
Bacon	20 mins	+20 mins	350°F, 20 mins before end raise to 375°F
Chicken	20 mins	+20 mins (longer if stuffed)	375°F
Turkey	20 mins	+20 mins	375°F
Duck	30-35 mins	–	375°F
Goose	15 mins	+5 mins	375°F
Venison	30 mins	+30 mins	start at 450°F, after 10 mins reduce to 375°F

Game bird	Total time
Guinea fowl	45-60 mins
Pheasant	40-50 mins
Grouse	20-30 mins
Partridge	20-25 mins
Woodcock	20-30 mins
Snipe	10-12 mins

Note: when roasting game birds start at 450°F, and after 10 mins reduce to 400°F.

INDEX

OTHER TITLES IN THIS SERIES FROM EYEBRIGHT

OUR HOUSE BOOK £7.95/$14.95
The Home Record Keeper ISBN 0 948751 00 2

Do you ever forget the telephone number of the plumber? Do you know what to do when water is pouring through the ceiling? Do you have anywhere to note the colour of the paint in the kitchen? Here is a book where all busy homeowners can record everything they need to keep the home running smoothly. It also contains notes to help you cope with emergencies as well as the basic utilities. A valuable addition to any home. Illustrated throughout with charming drawings.

OUR GARDEN BOOK £7.95/$14.95
The Garden Planner and Record Keeper ISBN 0 948751 01 0

A unique and practical book for all gardeners to keep their notes and plans. By helping you to plan improvements, keep a garden diary and note useful tips, this book could become your personal and invaluable garden manual, and enable you to achieve the garden of your dreams. Illustrated with beautiful watercolours throughout.

ORDER FORM
Note: If you don't want to spoil your book, make a photocopy of this coupon instead.

Please send me ____copies of OUR HOUSE BOOK @ £8.95 including post and packing/$26.95 air/$20.75 surface mail

Please send me ____copies of OUR GARDEN BOOK @ £8.95 including post and packing/$26.95 air/$20.75 surface mail

I enclose a cheque for a total of £_____made payable to Eyebright Publications at the following address:

21 Weedon Lane, Amersham, Bucks HP6 5QT, England. Allow 28 days for UK delivery

Name ____

Address ____

____ Post Code __________